FUN·WITH

DINOSAURS

MARYLEBONE
books

When did dinosaurs live?

Human beings have been living on Earth for the last two million years, but dinosaurs lived here long before that — and for a much longer time too. They lived during the time known as the Mesozoic Era, which began 225 million years ago and ended 65 million years ago. There were many types of dinosaur and they didn't all live at the same time. Scientists have divided the time into three ages: the Triassic age, when early dinosaurs like the Plateosaurus and the Coelophysis lived; the Jurassic age when dinosaurs like the Stegosaurus and the Brachiosaurus lived; and finally, the Cretaceous age when dinosaurs like the Triceratops and the Tyrannosaurus lived.

CRETACEOUS AGE
65-136 million years ago

JURASSIC AGE
136-196 million years ago

TRIASSIC AGE
196-225 million years ago

We didn't know anything at all about dinosaurs until last century when the first dinosaur fossils were found. A fossil is the remains of an animal or plant which has been buried in the earth for so long that it has eventually turned to stone. Everything we know about dinosaurs has come from finding more fossils and piecing the information together like a giant jigsaw puzzle. Dinosaurs' bones have also been found, as well as teeth, skin, eggs, droppings and footprints. All these help us to work out what the dinosaurs looked like, how they moved and what they ate, but no one can know for sure what colour they were or what kind of noises they made. The exciting thing about dinosaurs is that we are continually learning more about them as new discoveries are made.

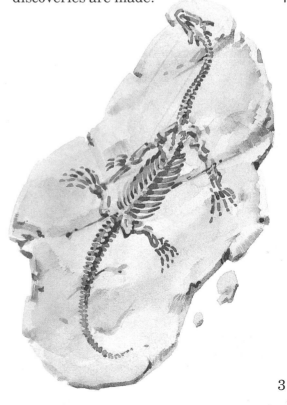

3

What were dinosaurs like?

The name dinosaur means 'terrible lizard', and many dinosaurs certainly were very terrible. Some, like the giant Tyrannosaurus, were meat-eaters (or carnivores) with huge, sharp teeth for tearing up their prey. Others were plant-eaters (or herbivores) and many of these had fierce-looking horns and spikes or bony 'armour' to protect them against predators. Many were gigantically tall, like the Brachiosaurus who could easily look over the top of one of today's three-storey buildings!

Many dinosaurs lived together in herds and they could often move extremely fast. They always carried their bodies clear of the ground — some walking on just their back legs and using their shorter, lighter fore-limbs rather like arms. Baby dinosaurs hatched out of eggs. Many died young, but if they survived they could live for about 100 years.

It seems strange that, after living on Earth for such a long time, dinosaurs should all die out quite suddenly about 65 million years ago, but that's what happened. There are lots of different theories about why this should be. Some scientists believe that a huge lump of rock about 10 kilometres (6 miles) in diameter collided with the Earth at around this time, resulting in months and months of darkness. Perhaps this meant that, because plants couldn't grow, the dinosaurs starved to death. Other people believe that a change in the weather was responsible for their extinction. During the age of the dinosaurs it was fairly mild and warm everywhere all year round, but about 65 million years ago the world's climate began to grow more seasonal, with warm summers and cold, harsh winters. Maybe the dinosaurs couldn't cope with the new, cold weather? Or maybe it was a combination of different reasons. Perhaps, one day, we will know.

Make an Eggboxosaurus

You will need:

- a large, oblong, cardboard box (big enough for you to get inside on all fours)
- lots of egg-boxes
- strong, non-toxic glue
- scissors
- paints and a brush

1. Cut off all the flaps from the top of the box and save the two longer ones.

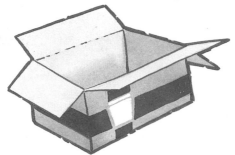

2. Turn the box upside down and ask a grown-up to cut a hole on the edge of one side, big enough for you to get your head through.

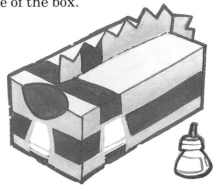

3. Make a back ridge for your dinosaur with one of the long cardboard flaps. Shorten it to fit from the hole to the end of the box, and then round off the corners. Cut out notches to make the finished shape. Fold a flap along the bottom and glue it along the top of the box.

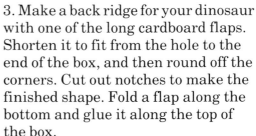

4. Make a ridged tail in the same way using the other flap. Glue it down the side of the box.

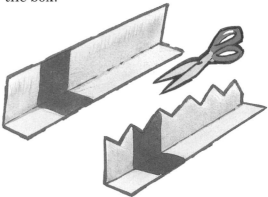

5. Cut your egg-boxes in half, and glue them all over the box.

6. Now paint your dinosaur any colours you like.

When it's dry your Eggboxosaurus will be ready to get into — you supply the head! If a friend, or brother or sister, makes one too you can have a crawling Eggboxosaurus race.

A Yoghurtpotosaurus is very effective too. Use small yoghurt pots instead of egg-boxes — but you'll need lots of pots!

The first dinosaur fossils were found in England in 1822 by Mary Mantell amongst a pile of stones near her home in Sussex. They turned out to be the huge teeth — 5 cm (2 in) long — of what we now call an Iguanodon.

A huge number of dinosaur fossils were found in the western part of North America during the late 19th century. So many fossil hunters rushed off there on expeditions that it became known as the 'dinosaur rush' — some even had to fight with Indians in order to get to the fossil sites.

Some plant-eating dinosaurs, like the Plateosaurus, didn't chew their food at all. Instead, they swallowed pieces of stone which stayed inside their stomach and would grind up the plants after they had swallowed them! The crocodile — a distant relative — still does this today.

Dinosaurs were probably good parents. The remains of several nests, made out of mud and sand, have been found — some with remains of quite grown-up young dinosaurs inside. This shows that their parents must have looked after them for a considerable length of time.

Not all dinosaurs had small brains. The Saurornithoides had a very large brain — six times as big as a crocodile of the same size — and must have been very intelligent.

How to eat a Stegosaurus

Although the Stegosaurus looked very fierce it was, in fact, a plant-eating dinosaur. It used its spikes to defend it from other dinosaurs who might want to eat it. *You* might want to eat this Stegosaurus, because it's made of delicious gingerbread — and it's fun to make too! Ask a grown-up to help with the cooking part.

You will need:

> baking tray
> sieve
> mixing bowl
> saucepan
> wooden spoon
> rolling-pin
> round-ended knife
> wire cooling rack
> thin card
> pencil, scissors
> tracing paper or greaseproof paper
>
> 250 g (10 oz) self-raising flour
> 2 teaspoons ground ginger
> a pinch of salt
> 50 g (2 oz) margarine
> 75 g (3 oz) castor sugar
> 3 tablespoons golden syrup
> about 100 g (4 oz) blanched almonds
> glacé cherries or silver balls
> some thin strips of angelica

1. Trace round the outline of the Stegosaurus given here and transfer the tracing on to your card. Cut it out to make a template.

2. Turn on the oven to Gas Mark 6 or 200° C (400° F).

3. Grease a large baking tray with a little extra margarine.

4. Sieve the flour, ginger and salt into a mixing bowl.

5. Put the margarine, sugar and golden syrup into a saucepan and melt them together over a gentle heat, stirring with a wooden spoon.

6. Pour the melted mixture into the bowl, mixing well, until you have a small ball of dough.

7. While it is still warm, roll out the dough on a lightly-floured work surface until it is about 1 cm (½ in) thick.

8. Put your template on to the dough and cut carefully round it with a knife. Place the Stegosaurus on the baking tray. Roll out and repeat until all the dough is used up. (You could use any left-over scraps to make Stegosaurus eggs.)

9. Now stick almonds all along the Stegosaurus's back to make its spiky 'armour'. Make sure you stick them in well, or they may fall out during cooking. Use a tiny piece of glacé cherry or a silver ball for its eye and two strips of angelica to make the spikes at the end of its tail.

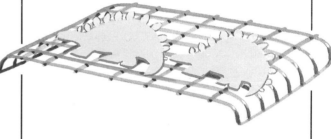

10. Bake for 8-10 minutes until firm and lightly golden. Then slide them carefully on to a wire rack to cool.

Make your own Prehistoric Landscape

The next few pages make up a pull-out section which you can use as a frieze to put up on your wall or as a backdrop for playing with model dinosaurs. Or why not try making your own three-dimensional landscape?

You will need:

> an old tray or baking tray
> some small stones or pebbles
> sand
> some twigs
> the top of a jar

1. Stand the pull-out section at the back of the tray.

2. Fill the jar top with water and stand it on the tray to make a pool.

3. Spread sand over the remaining surface and pile up stones or pebbles to make hills.

4. Stick twigs in amongst the stones to make trees.

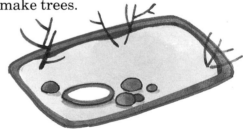

5. Put model dinosaurs in the scene and act out their adventures and battles.

Next time you have an egg for breakfast, use the shell to make a model of a newly-hatched baby dinosaur. When you've finished, put it in someone's egg-cup and give them a surprise!

You will need:

 an empty eggshell
 modelling clay
 paints or felt-tips

1. Mould your clay into a baby dinosaur shape like this one.

2. Carefully decorate the eggshell with paint or felt-tips.

3. Put the baby dinosaur inside the shell, with its face peeping out.

If you haven't got any modelling clay you can make your own.

You will need:

 3 cups of plain white flour
 1 cup of salt
 ½ teaspoon cooking oil
 a few drops of food colouring
 water
 mixing bowl

1. Mix the flour, salt, oil and food colouring together in a bowl.

2. Add enough water to make a dough.

3. Knead the dough well until it's soft, stretchy and ready to use!

If you don't use all the modelling dough, put it inside an airtight container and it will stay moist for a long time.

19

Terrible Dinosaur Jokes!

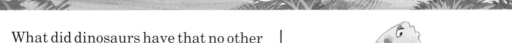

What did dinosaurs have that no other living creature has?

Baby dinosaurs!

Where does a Tyrannosaurus sleep when it comes to stay?

Anywhere it wants to!

Why did the dinosaur lose the competition against the porcupine?

The porcupine won on points!

What did they call prehistoric sailing disasters?

Tyrannosaurus wrecks!

Can you name ten dinosaurs in five seconds?

Yes, eight Stegosauruses and two Iguanodons!

What time is it when a Brachiosaurus rides on your bicycle?

Time to get a new bicycle!

What do you call a dinosaur that's as tall as a house, with huge pointed teeth, twelve gigantic claws on each hand and a personal stereo over its ears?

Anything you like, he'll never hear you!

What would you get if you crossed a Triceratops with a mouse?

Gigantic holes in the skirting board!

What do you call a dinosaur that's as tall as a house, with huge pointed teeth and twelve gigantic claws on each hand?

Sir!

How do you know if there's a dinosaur in bed with you?

By the 'D' on his pyjamas!

How do you know if there's a Brachiosaurus in bed with you?

By the dinosnores!

21

More Fascinating Facts

In 1911 an eleven-year-old English girl called Mary Aming found the entire skeleton of an Ichthyosaurus near her home in Lyme Regis in Dorset. She had started collecting — and selling — fossils when she was ten years old.

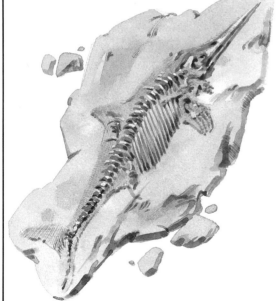

In 1972 parts of a dinosaur even bigger than the gigantic Brachiosaurus were discovered in Colorado, USA. It has been named 'Supersaurus', and was more than 15 m (49 ft) tall and up to 30 m (98 ft) long! Then, in 1979, more bones of an even bigger dinosaur were found. This hasn't been named yet, but its nickname is 'Ultrasaurus'.

The fossils of 'armour-plated' dinosaurs like the Palaeoscincus are usually discovered upside down. This is because their bodies have been washed into rivers or the sea and the weight of their armoured backs has turned them over in the water.

The Tyrannosaurus is the largest known meat-eating animal which has ever lived on land. It is often called 'Tyrannosaurus Rex' — *rex* meaning 'king' in Latin. The Tyrannosaurus must have been a horrible sight — its head alone was 1.25 m (4 ft) long!

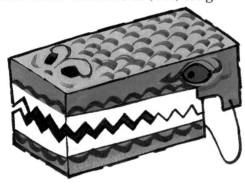

You will need:

  2 'man-size' tissue boxes
  scissors
  strong paste and a brush
  thick paint or felt-tips
  plain coloured paper
  sticky tape
  2 strips of white paper 3 cm x 16 cm
                    (1¼ in x 6¼ in)
  4 strips of white paper 3 cm x 22 cm
                    (1¼ in x 8¾ in)
  a piece of elastic long enough to
    stretch comfortably around your
    head

1. Take your first box (Box A) and cut as shown.

2. Open out the top. If the ends start to come apart, glue them back again.

3. Cut 10 cm (4 in) off the end of your second box (Box B). Throw the smaller piece away.

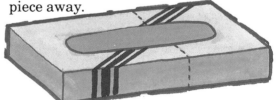

4. Make cuts at the other end of Box B as you did with Box A and open out.

5. Colour in the outside of both boxes with thick paints or felt-tips, or cover with coloured paper. Leave to dry.

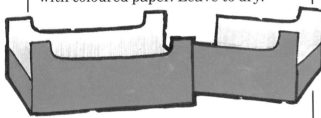

6. Glue a 3 cm x 16 cm (1¼ in x 6¼ in) strip of white paper across one short end of Box A and another across the end of Box B. Cut notches into each strip to form teeth.

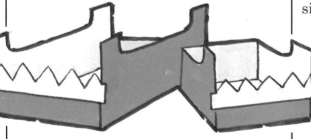

7. Cut a curved section, about 4 cm (1½ in) deep at the centre, out of the other short end of Box A.

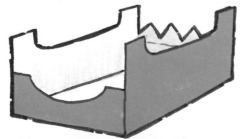

8. Cut a larger curved section, about 7 cm (3 in) deep, out of the bottom of the other end of Box B.

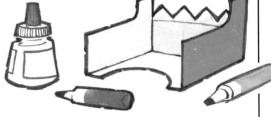

9. Put Box A over Box B so that the teeth match. Tilt the back of Box B so that the back corners overlap Box A by about 1 cm (½ in) at the back. Now stick the two boxes together along the sides with sticky tape.

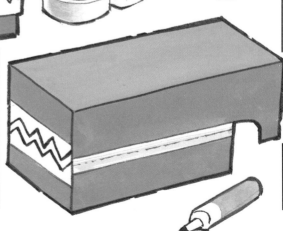

10. Take your four remaining strips of white paper and cut notches in them for more teeth. Glue two on to each side of the mask, joining them on to the existing teeth at one end and just overlapping each other at the other end. Cut out the cardboard between the first few notches at the front to make a gaping jaw.

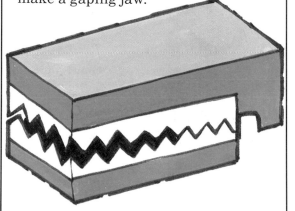

11. Paint on eyes at the side of your mask, and nostrils at the top.

12. Pierce two holes at the side of the mask at the back and thread the elastic through. Knot the ends and secure at the holes with sticky tape.

25

How much do you know about dinosaurs?

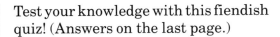

Test your knowledge with this fiendish quiz! (Answers on the last page.)

1. Dinosaurs lived on Earth for:
a) about 12 million years.
b) about 25 million years.
c) about 160 million years.

2. A scientist who studies dinosaur fossils is called a:
a) palaeontologist.
b) pharmacologist.
c) psychologist.

3. Which of these dinosaurs had a 'sail' on its back?
a) Iguanodon.
b) Spinosaurus.
c) Protoceratops.

4. What would the teeth of a carnivorous dinosaur look like?
a) Pointed with saw-like edges.
b) A strong, flat surface for grinding.
c) Weak with rounded ends.

5. What does the name of a Struthiomimus mean?
a) 'Thunder dinosaur'.
b) 'Ostrich dinosaur'.
c) 'Terrible claw'.

6. How long was a single Tyrannosaurus tooth?
a) As long as a man's thumb.
b) As long as a pen.
c) As long as a walking-stick.

7. Which of these dinosaurs had a spiky neck-frill?

a) Stegosaurus.
b) Apatosaurus.
c) Styracosaurus.

9. Which of these dinosaurs had a crested skull?

a) Parasaurolophus.
b) Diplodocus.
c) Camptosaurus.

8. What would a Triceratops have eaten?

a) Other dinosaurs.
b) Plants and vegetation.
c) Lizards and insects.

10. How many different sorts of dinosaur have so far been discovered?

a) About 100.
b) About 250.
c) About 350.

Make a Life-Size Coelophysis

The Coelophysis (pronounced Seel-oh-fy-sis) was a meat-eating dinosaur which lived in North America in the Triassic age. Why not try making a life-size drawing of one? You might even be able to put it up on the wall when you've finished!

You will need:

25 sheets of paper, each 30 cm x 42 cm
                            (12 in x 16¾ in)
pencil
paints, crayons or felt-tips
clear sticky tape

1. Pencil a small number in the corner of each sheet from 1-25.

2. Take sheet number 1 and copy, as exactly as you can, the lines of the drawing in rectangle 1 of the picture here.

3. Now take sheet 2 and copy the lines in rectangle 2 — hold it next to your sheet 1 to make sure that the lines match at the join.

4. Carry on with each sheet, holding it against the ones around it until you have finished the whole outline.

5. Stick the sheets together until you have a complete, life-sized Coelophysis! (If you can, stick the sheets by taping at the back of the picture — then it'll be easier to colour in).

6. Colour the entire picture with paints, crayons or felt-tips.

If a life-size Coelophysis is just a bit too big for you, you can make a smaller one using smaller sheets of paper.

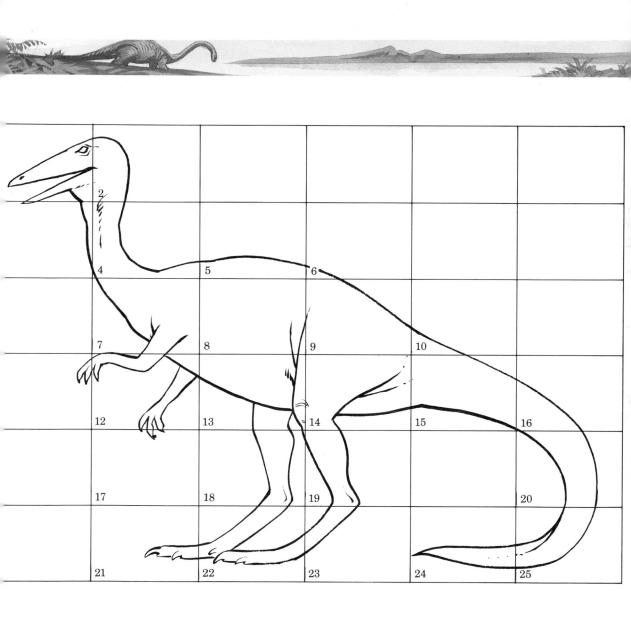

'How much do you know about dinosaurs?' — The Answers

Give yourself one point for every correct answer.

1. c	6. b
2. a	7. c
3. b	8. b
4. a	9. a
5. b	10. c.

How did you score?

0-1

Oh dear..! Never mind — you've probably learnt more just by doing this quiz!

2-4

Not bad. You probably know more than most people, but you've still got lots to learn.

5-7

Very good! You're well on your way to becoming an expert.

8-10

Brilliant! You certainly know a lot about dinosaurs — maybe you'd like to be a palaeontologist yourself!

This edition produced exclusively for Marylebone Books in 1987 by
Cathay Books Ltd
59 Grosvenor Street
London W1

Text by Stella Kebby
Illustrated by John Francis

Copyright © 1987 Cathay Books Ltd

ISBN 0 86178 477 4

Produced by Mandarin Publishers Ltd, Hong Kong